THE JOY OF
LISZT

WISE PUBLICATIONS
part of The Music Sales Group

London / New York / Paris / Sydney / Copenhagen / Berlin / Hong Kong / Tokyo / Madrid

Published by
Wise Publications
14-15 Berners Street, London W1T 3LJ, UK.

Exclusive Distributors:
Music Sales Limited
Distribution Centre, Newmarket Road, Bury St. Edmunds, Suffolk IP33 3YB, UK.
Music Sales Corporation
Music Sales Corporation, 180 Madison Avenue, 24th Floor, New York NY 10016, USA.
Music Sales Pty Limited
Music Sales Pty., Units 3-4, 17 Willfox Street, Condell Park, NSW 2200, Australia.

Order No. AM1009481
ISBN: 978-1-78305-718-4
This book © Copyright 2014 Wise Publications,
a division of Music Sales Limited.

Edited by Sam Lung.
Music engraved by Elius Gravure Musicale.
Cover designed by Tim Field.

Printed in the EU.

Your Guarantee of Quality
As publishers, we strive to produce every book to the highest commercial standards.
This book has been carefully designed to minimise awkward page turns and to make playing from it a real pleasure.
Particular care has been given to specifying acid-free, neutral-sized paper made from
pulps which have not been elemental chlorine bleached.
This pulp is from farmed sustainable forests and was produced with special regard for the environment.
Throughout, the printing and binding have been planned to ensure a sturdy,
attractive publication which should give years of enjoyment.
If your copy fails to meet our high standards, please inform us and we will gladly replace it.

www.musicsales.com

Eclogue

No.7 *from* Années de Pèlerinage I, S.160

Franz Liszt

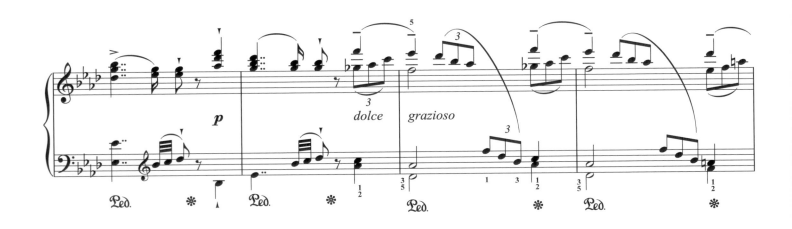

Petrarch's 123rd Sonnet

No.6 *from* Années de Pèlerinage II, S.161

Franz Liszt

Angelus! Prayer to the Guardian Angels

No.1 *from* Années de Pèlerinage III, S.163

(for Harmonium or Piano)

Franz Liszt

18

Bagatelle sans tonalité

'Mephisto Waltz', S.216a

Franz Liszt

Cantique d'amour

No.10 *from* Harmonies poétiques et religieuses III, S.173

Franz Liszt

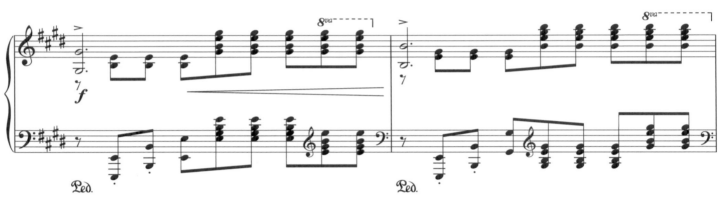

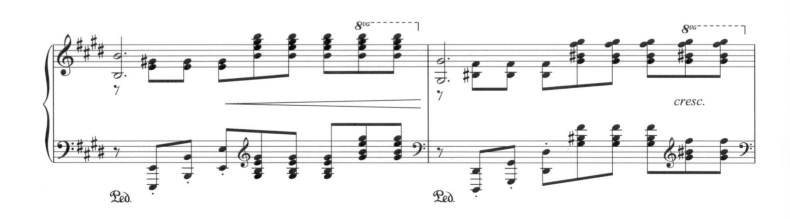

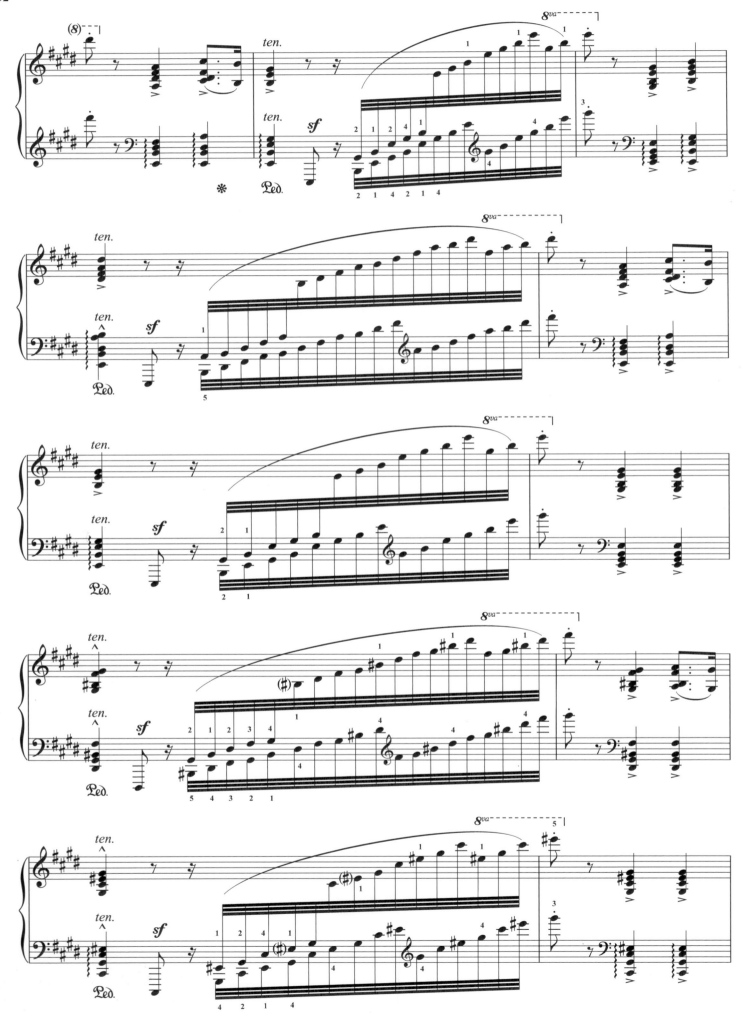

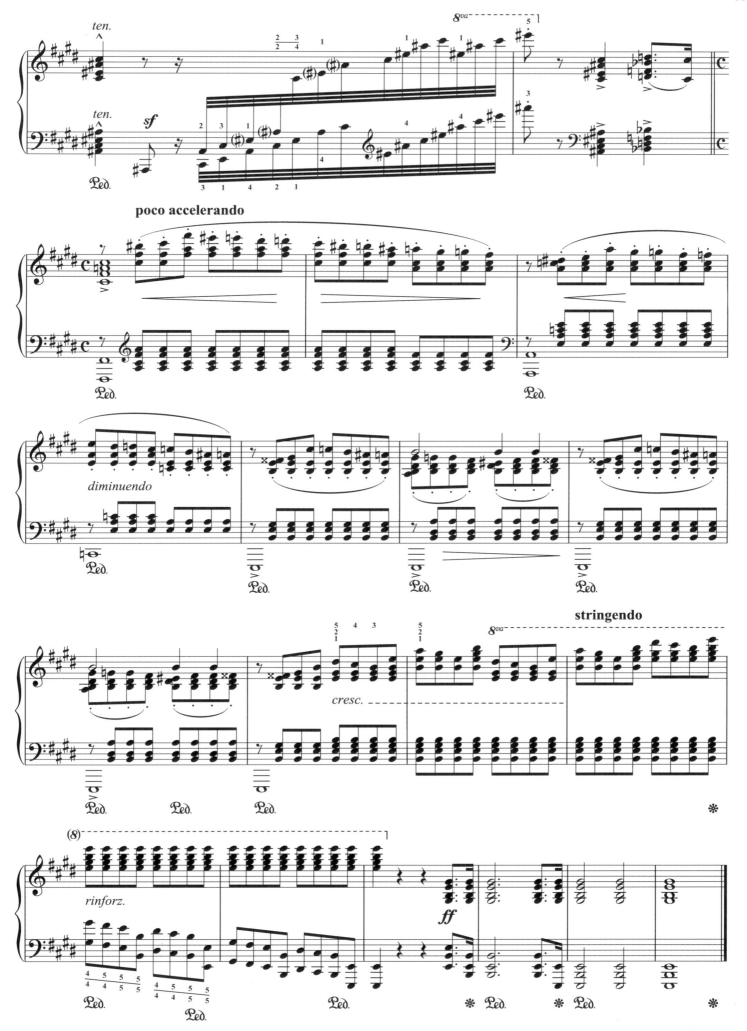

Consolation No.1

Franz Liszt

Consolation No.3

Franz Liszt

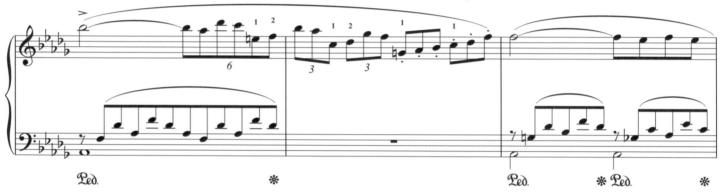

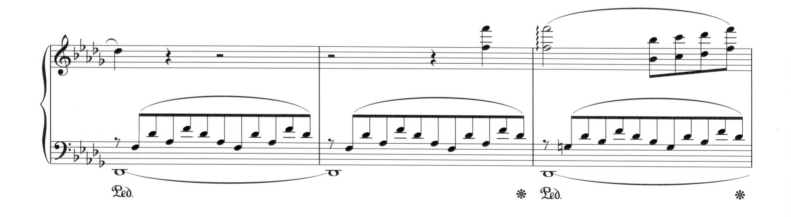

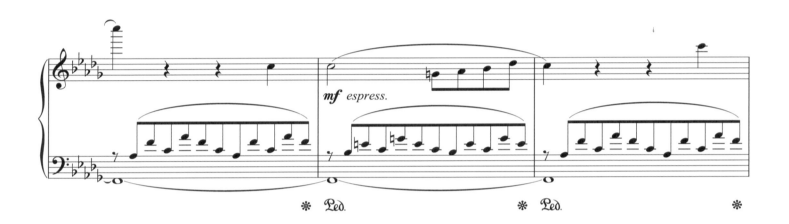

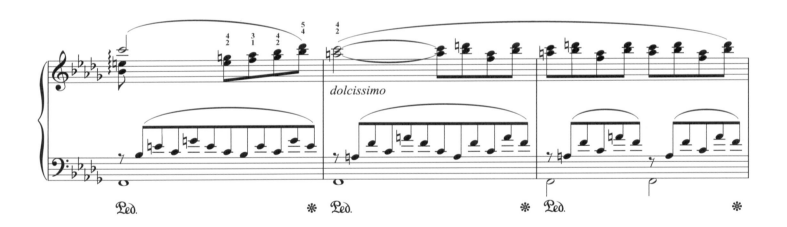

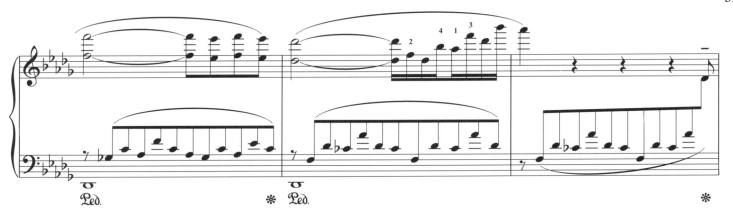

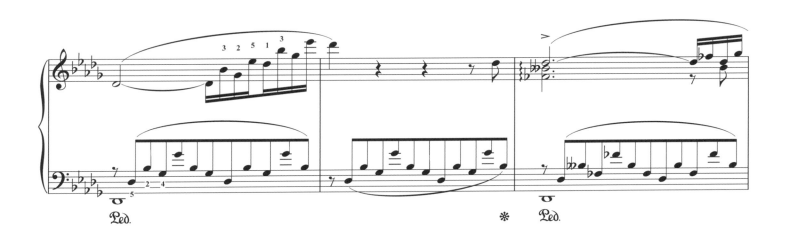

Consolation No.5

Franz Liszt

Un sospiro

from 3 Études de concert, S.144

Franz Liszt

44

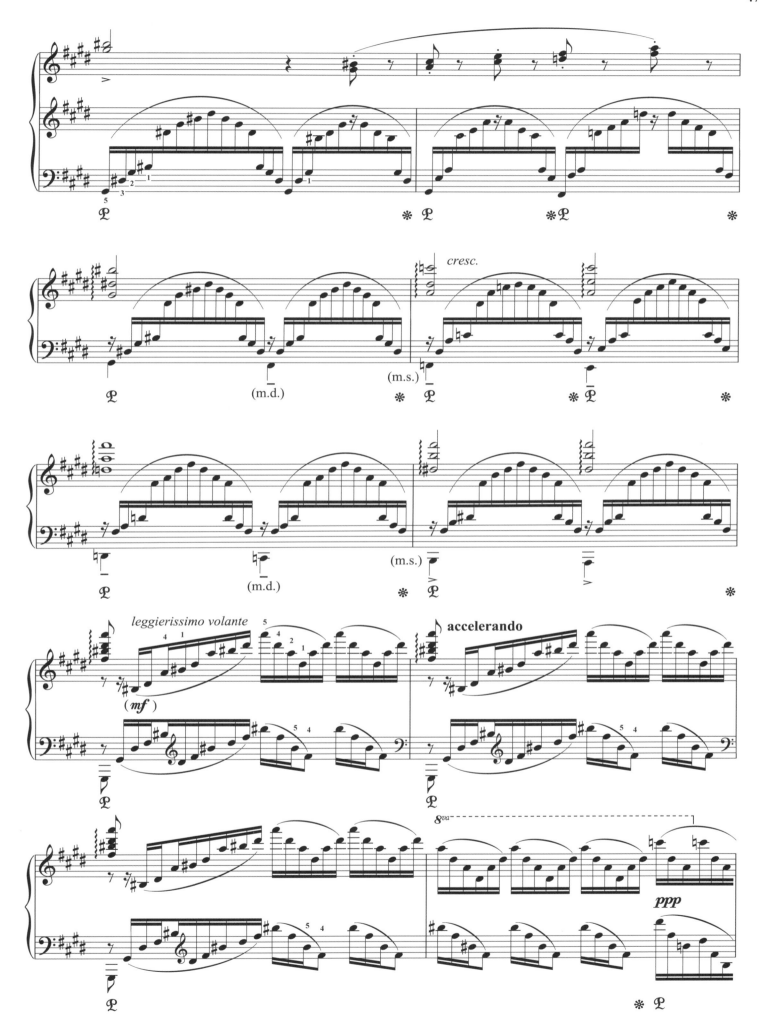

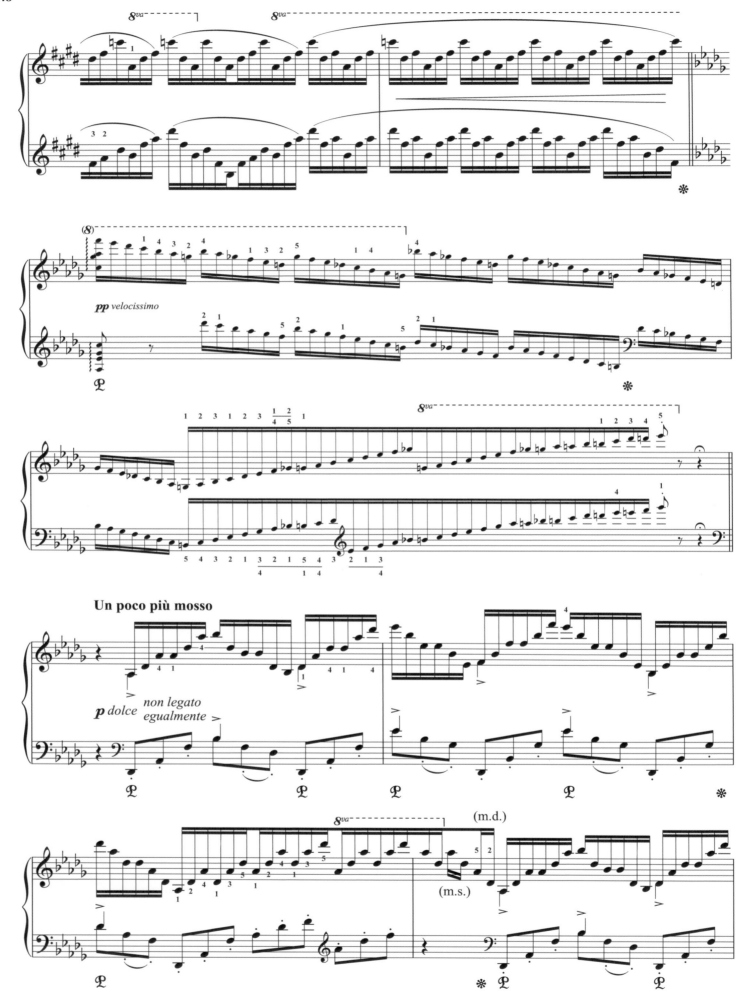

50

Elegy No.2
S.197

Franz Liszt

54

En rêve (Nocturne)

S.207

Franz Liszt

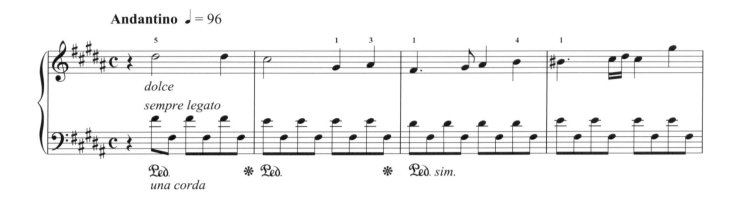

58

Rakoczy March

S.244c

Franz Liszt

64

Valse-Impromptu
S.213

Franz Liszt

66

sempre dolce e scherzando

sempre dolce e scherzando

Valse oubliée No.1

from Valses oubliées ('Forgotten Waltzes'), S.215

Franz Liszt

80